GATEWAY TO IMAGINATION™

A Book Club from Discovery Toys

Open a book and unlock your
gateway to imagination

From the Library of

Kathleen Sullivan

Item #962   12/87

This edition is
published and distributed
exclusively by
DISCOVERY TOYS
Martinez, CA

First published
in 1988 by
Walker Books, Ltd.
London

Printed in Italy

ISBN 0-939979-22-5

Going Places

Written by
Frances Lawton

Illustrated by
Deborah Ward

DISCOVERY TOYS

We like going to all kinds of places.

We bring home lots of different things.

Today we brought home:

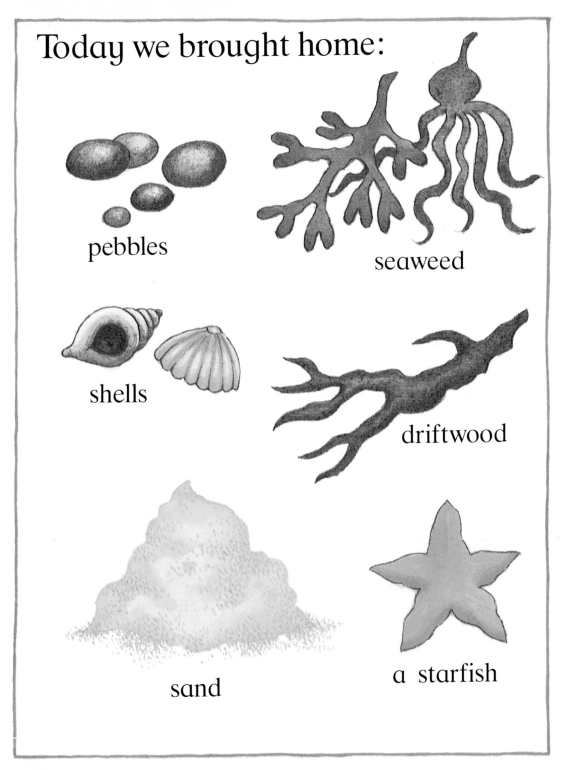

pebbles

seaweed

shells

driftwood

sand

a starfish

Guess where we have been today.

To the beach.

Today we brought home:

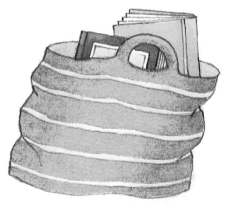

a tote bag

a story book

a picture book

badges

a file card

a counting book

Guess where we have been today.

To the library.

Today we brought home:

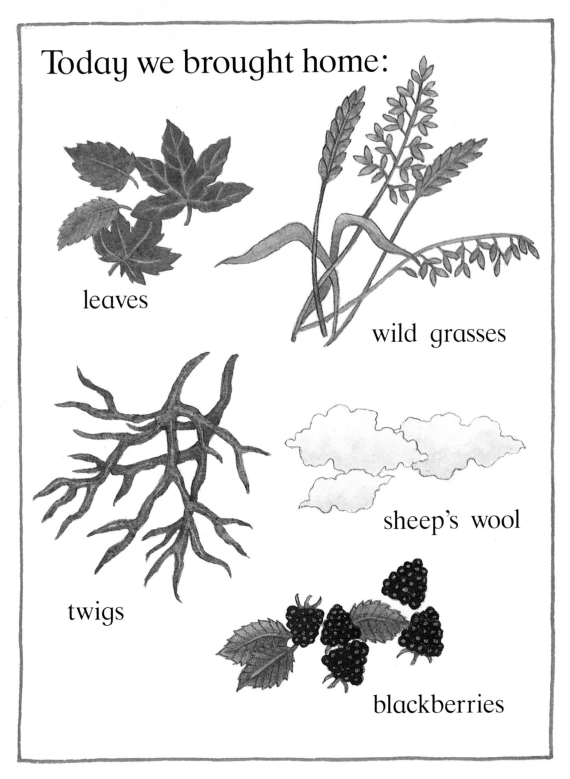

leaves

wild grasses

twigs

sheep's wool

blackberries

Guess where we have been today.

To the country.

Today we brought home:

oranges

bananas

a pineapple

carrots

potatoes

a purse

a cucumber

Guess where we have been today.

To the grocery store.

Today we brought home:

a mask

paper flowers

a painting

a card

a model ship

Guess where we have been today.

To playgroup.

Today we brought home:

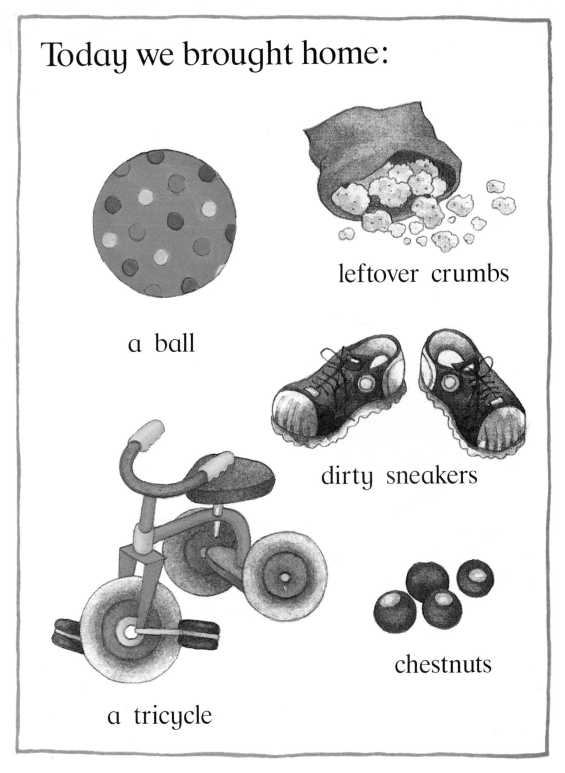

a ball

leftover crumbs

dirty sneakers

chestnuts

a tricycle

Guess where we have been today.

To the park.

Today we brought home:

bread

spaghetti

cans of food

a shopping list

cookies

butter

Guess where we have been today.

To the supermarket.

Today we brought home:

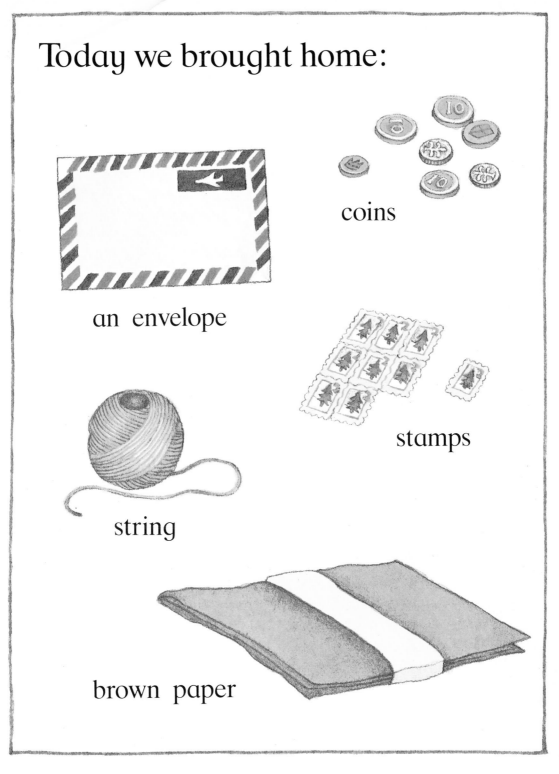

coins

an envelope

stamps

string

brown paper

Guess where we have been today.

To the post office.

Today we brought home:

candy

a balloon

a piece of cake

a noisemaker

a hat

Guess where we have been today.

To a party.

Today we brought home:

muddy boots

straw

fresh eggs

apples

hens' feathers

Guess where we have been today.

To the farm.